Walt Disney's

Davy Crockett

KING OF THE WILD FRONTIER

Illustrated by The Walt Disney Studios

Adapted by Mel Crawford

Story by Irwin Shapiro

Reader's Digest
Children's Books™

Pleasantville, New York • Montréal, Québec • Bath, United Kingdom

Long ago, America was a land of woods and forests.
And deep in the green woods, high on a mountain top, a baby
was born. His Ma and his Pa called him Davy—Davy Crockett.
And it happened in the state of Tennessee.

Little Davy was raised in the woods. He learned to know every tree. He learned to know the critters, too. From the little possum to the big bear, Davy knew them all.

As Davy grew up, he learned how to shoot. He was a real rip-snorter with a rifle.

Once a bear came at Davy from one side. A panther came at him from the other side. Davy fired his rifle at a rock between them. The bullet hit the rock, splitting into two pieces. One piece hit the bear, the other hit the panther. That way, Davy got him two critters with one shot.

No mistake about it—Davy was one of the greatest hunters that ever was.

He liked to tell the story of the time he saw a raccoon up a tree. Before he raised his rifle, Davy grinned at the raccoon.

"Don't shoot, Davy! I'll come down!" said the raccoon.

It wasn't long before Davy tried his grin on a bear. He looked the bear right in the eye. The bear looked Davy right in the eye. Davy grinned and grinned, trying to grin that bear to death.

Then, snarling and growling, the bear rushed at Davy.

"Well, bear," said Davy, "guess we'll have to fight."
And they did. They rolled through the bushes, shaking the ground like an earthquake.

Davy won the fight, of course. But he had to give up grinning at bears. He saved his grin for the little critters, like the raccoons and the possums.

Besides hunting, Davy liked fun and frolics. He was always ready to dance. He'd stomp and step with the other folks, singing:

Old Dan Tucker was a good old man,
Washed his face in a frying pan,
Combed his hair with a wagon wheel,
And died with a toothache in his heel.

But when the Indians started a war, Davy stopped his hunting
and dancing. With his friend, George Russel, he joined General
Andy Jackson's army.

They fought the Indians in the forest and the swamp.

Davy was a brave fighter, and a good fighter. And yet, he did not like war.

As soon as he could, Davy helped make peace with the Indians. After that, he and the Indians were friends.

Folks liked Davy's way of doing things. They thought Davy ought to be a Congressman and help run the country. The critters seemed to think so, too. Even the crickets chirped:

"Crockett for Congress! Crockett for Congress!"

At least, they sounded like that to Davy.

Sure enough, Davy was elected to Congress. He went to the nation's capitol in Washington City. There he made a speech.

He said, "I'm Davy Crockett, fresh from the backwoods. I'm half horse, half alligator, and a little tetched with snappin' turtle. I have the fastest horse, the prettiest sister, the surest rifle, and the ugliest dog in Tennessee."

Folks all over the country were talking about Davy. They wanted to see him. They wanted to hear his funny stories. Davy took a trip, stopping in the cities to make speeches.

In Philadelphia, the folks gave him a fine new rifle. Davy liked it so much he called it old Betsy.

Davy could hardly wait to get back to the woods and try out old Betsy. But more and more folks were making their homes in the forest. It was getting too crowded for Davy.

He and George Russel went west, where there was more room.
They traveled part of the way by boat.

At last Davy and George reached the west. They saw the wide, wide prairies. They saw the tall, tall grass. They saw the herds of wild buffalo.

"This is a fine country," said Davy. "It's worth fighting for. Guess we'll head for the fort called the Alamo, where the Texans are fighting for liberty."

Whatever Davy said, he did.
He helped fight a great battle at the Alamo.

Ever since, folks have told stories about Davy. They tell about Davy riding a streak of lightning.

And they tell of Davy catching a comet by the tail, before it could crash into the earth. Davy threw the comet back into the sky, where it couldn't do any harm.

Another story folks tell is of the time of the Big Freeze. It was so cold the sun and earth were frozen, and couldn't move.

Davy saw that he would have to do something. He climbed up
Daybreak Hill. He thawed out the sun and the earth with hot bear
oil. Then he gave the earth's cogwheel a kick, and got things mov-
ing.

As the sun rose, Davy walked down the hill, with a piece of sun-
rise in his pocket.

And some folks say that Davy is still roaming the woods.
And right with Davy is his friend, George Russel, singing:
Born on a mountain top in Tennessee,
Greenest state in the Land of the Free,
Raised in the woods so's he knew every tree,
Kilt him a b'ar when he was only three.
Davy—Davy Crockett,
King of the Wild Frontier!